Beverley Craven

Music Arranged by Roger Day
Music Processed by Musicprint Limited
© Copyright 1991 Warner Chappell Music Limited,
London W1Y 3FA
Photographs by Neil McKenzie-Matthews

Promise Me

You light up another cigarette
And I pour the wine
It's four o'clock in the morning
And it's starting to get light
Now I'm right where I want to be
Losing track of time
But I wish that it was still last night

You look like you're in another world
But I can read your mind
How can you be so far away
Lying by my side
When I go away I'll miss you
And I will be thinking of you
Every night and day, just . . .

Promise me you'll wait for me
'Cause I'll be saving all my love for you
And I will be home soon
Promise me you'll wait for me
I need to know you feel the same way too
And I'll be home, I'll be home soon

When I go away I'll miss you
And I will be thinking of you
Every night and day, just . . .

Promise me you'll wait for me
'Cause I'll be saving all my love for you
And I will be home soon
Promise me you'll wait for me
I need to know you feel the same way too
And I'll be home, I'll be home soon

Promise me you'll wait for me
'Cause I'll be saving all my love for you
And I will be home soon
Promise me you'll wait for me
I need to know you feel the same way too
And I'll be home, I'll be home soon

PROMISE ME

Words and Music by
BEVERLEY CRAVEN

5

Holding On

I'm losing control of my emotions
You've got this hold on my heart,
I've never known what we are feeling
You never took me so far.
I can't find the words
Is this love?
Tell me I've found you.
Is this love?
say that you'll always keep. . .

    Holding on
    Keep holding on
    'Cos your love's got a hold on me
    Holding on
    Keep holding on
    Yeah . . .

I'm losing my mind dreaming about you
Still as you sleep by my side
Kiss me awake, whisper good-morning
Say what you said one more time
'Cos I need to know
Is this love?
tell me I've found you.
Is this love?
say that you'll always keep. . .

    Holding on
    Keep holding on
    'Cos your love's got a hold on me
    Holding on
    Keep holding on
    Yeah . . .

Is this love?
Tell me I've found you
Is this love?
Say that you'll always keep

    Holding on
    Keep holding on
    'Cos your love's got a hold on me
    Holding on
    Keep holding on
    Yeah . . .

HOLDING ON

Words and Music by
BEVERLEY CRAVEN

13

Woman to Woman

Everytime you get a new boyfriend
I don't see you for weeks on end.
when I call 'cause I need to talk
I feel like I'm taking up your time.
There are things that I can only say
To a woman and face to face.
but you're occupied almost every night
I've got a secret and I need advice,

   Woman to woman
   He came and took possession
   Now you never come around and talk
   Woman to woman
   No —
   Because I don't matter now you've fallen in love

Two is company and three's a crowd
Like my father I'm much too proud
If it falls apart and he breaks your heart
There'll be tears on the telephone again
And where are you when I'm the one who needs
Consolation while my heart bleeds
Saying, "look it's late, can I break our date?"
Did no one tell you that it's give and take?

   Woman to woman
   He came and took possession
   Now you never come around and talk
   Woman to woman
   No —
   Because I don't matter now you've fallen in love

WOMAN TO WOMAN

Words and Music by
BEVERLEY CRAVEN

Moderate, strong beat

(1.) Ev - 'ry time you get a
(2.) Two is com - pa - ny and

new boy - friend _____ I don't see ___ you for weeks on end. _____
three's a crowd _____ like my fa - ther I'm much too proud. ___ If it

when I call _____ 'cause I need to talk ___ I feel ___
falls a - part ___ and he breaks your heart, ___ there'll be tears ___

Memories

My little sister sings herself to sleep
She doesn't know we're listening to her lullaby
So innocent and sweet
I've rocked her cradle till her tears were dry
And chased away a sleepless night with a fairy-tale
Reliving the best years of my life
When I look into her eyes
And then I realise

    Everything she's going through
    Will be her memories
    When she's older and wiser
    She's making her history
    And everything we're going through
    Will be our memories
    I'm gonna make them worth remembering
    For years . . .

I'm gonna tell her when she wants to know
But in the end she's on her own
No more fairy-tales
Just giving the best years of her life
As a mother or a wife
A woman with a child

    Everything she's going through
    Will be her memories
    When she's older and wiser
    She's making her history
    And everything we're going through
    Will be our memories
    I'm gonna make them worth remembering
    For years . . .

MEMORIES

Words and Music by
BEVERLEY CRAVEN

Castle in the Clouds

You can waste your time building barriers
Spend your life trying to break them down again
Like an island in a sea that breathes revenge
When we talk sometimes you're a looking glass
Every word from the blueprint of your past
In the distance there's a castle in the clouds

    And our love will make us strong together
    We can be in love forever
    Just the two of us
    When I get lonely, hold me
    We will understand each other
    You will be my friend and lover
    When we're far apart
    You're in my heart I'm in your dreams

So you call a friend up for company
Drown your tears at a table set for three
There's a shoulder and a change of scenery
But when you wake tomorrow you're back again
And you wonder where it's all going to end
In the distance there's a castle in the clouds

    And our love will make us strong together
    We can be in love forever
    Just the two of us
    When I get lonely, hold me
    We will understand each other
    You will be my friend and lover
    When we're far apart
    You're in my heart I'm in your dreams

CASTLE IN THE CLOUDS

Words and Music by
BEVERLEY CRAVEN

Ballad, poco rubato

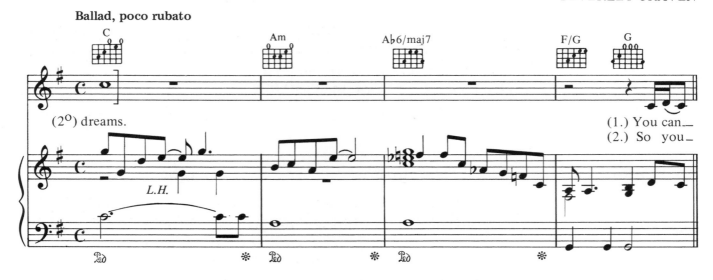

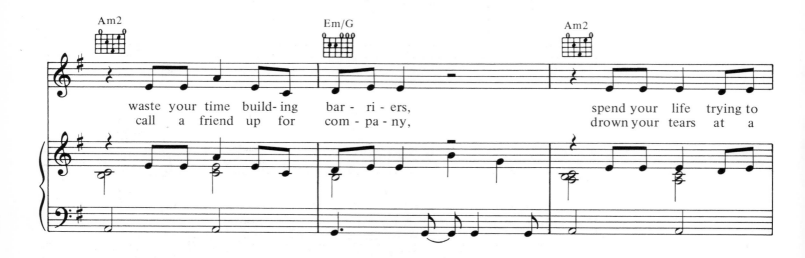

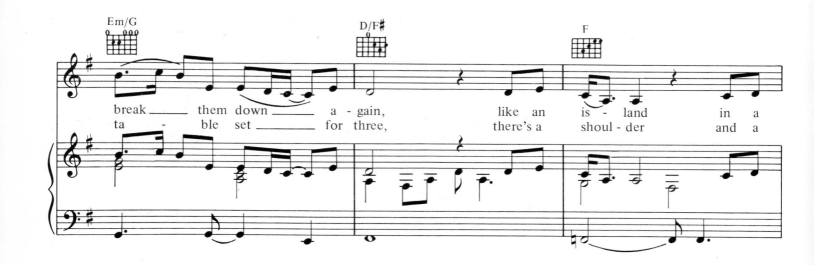

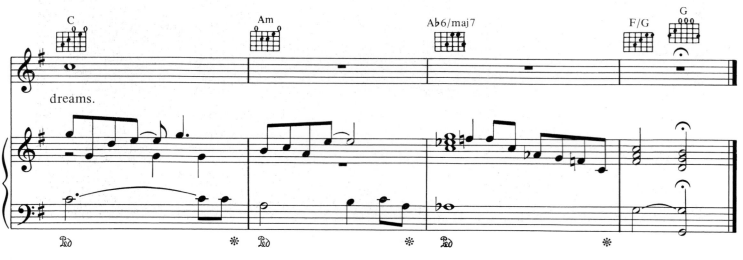

just the two of__ us, __ when I get__ lone - ly, hold me, __

we will un-der - stand_ each oth - er, you will be my_ friend_ and lo - ver_

when we're far a - part, __ you're in my heart, I'm in __ your

dreams.

You're Not the First

Just because there are rules
It doesn't mean the game is fair,
So you head the revolution
In your own illusion of despair.

Where were you a year ago today
Don't lose your faith

> You're not the first and you won't be the last
> Some day all this pain will pass
> With someone to care for
> And be there for always

When you kill the conversation
And make it hard to say goodbye,
I just hate the situation
But you get drunk and I'm just tired.

That was over years ago
Now I won't change my mind

> You're not the first and you won't be the last
> Some day all this pain will pass
> With someone to care for
> And be there for always
> Analysing everything to find some peace of mind

> You're not the first
> And you won't be the last
> Some day all this pain will pass
> With someone to care for
> And be there for always

YOU'RE NOT THE FIRST

Words and Music by
BEVERLEY CRAVEN

Joey

The first time that I saw you I went head over heels
You were the one for me
I just adore you see I'm down on my knees
And now we've found each other I could never leave

    Joey, I've fallen in love, oh yeah
    Joey, you're all I'll ever need
    Joey, I've fallen in love, oh yeah
    Joey, you're all I'll ever need

Sometimes when I feel like I'm fighting the world
I know you're on my side
They're trying to control me with their promises now
But we've still got each other when they try to get us down

    Joey, I've fallen in love, oh yeah
    Joey, you're all I'll ever need
    Joey, I've fallen in love, oh yeah
    Joey, you're all I'll ever need

You're part of my life
Every day I need your love more
Oh and I'll never give you up
Is it me you're looking for . . .

    Joey, I've fallen in love, oh yeah
    Joey, you're all I'll ever need
    Joey, I've fallen in love, oh yeah
    Joey, you're all I'll ever need

JOEY

Words and Music by
BEVERLEY CRAVEN

Relaxed beat (♩.)

(1.) The

first time— that I saw you— I went head ov- er heels

you were the one _____ for me _____

Jo - ey _____ I've fall - en in love _____ oh yeah _____

Jo - ey _____ you're all _____ I'll ev - er need. _____

Solo

Jo - ey _____ you're all _____ I'll ev - er need. _____

Jo - ey _____ I've fall-en in love _____ oh yeah, _____

Repeat ad lib. to Fade

Jo - ey _____ you're all _____ I'll ev - er need. _____

VERSE 2:
Sometimes when I feel like
I'm fighting the world
I know you're on my side
They're trying to control me
With their promises now
But we've still got each other
When they try and get us down.

Two of a Kind

How can you stand this waiting around
For the telephone to ring,
You want him bad but you can't let it show
'Cos you're scared of losing him.
He lets you down when he stands you up
And you swear he's history
But you've got no choice when you hear his voice
Saying, make love to me, make love to me

   . . . One more time
   He keeps you on the borderline
   He's got a one track mind
   And I can see by your smile
   That you're two of a kind
   Two of a kind

You say it's only a matter of time
And there must be someone else,
You wanna trust in his promises
But you'll never fool yourself.
Now you're reading into his every move
Like he only tells you lies
And then you're on the phone and he's on his own
Saying "come round tonight, make love to me"

   . . . One more time
   He keeps you on the borderline
   He's got a one track mind
   And I can see by your smile
   That you're two of a kind
   Two of a kind

   . . . One more time
   He keeps you on the borderline
   He's got a one track mind
   And I can see by your smile
   That you're two of a kind

   He's got you on the borderline
   He keeps you on the borderline
   He's got a one track mind
   nd I can see by your smile
   That you're two of a kind

TWO OF A KIND

Words and Music by
BEVERLEY CRAVEN

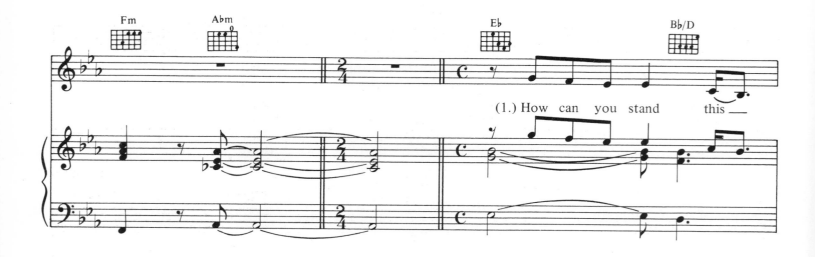

(1.) How can you stand this ___

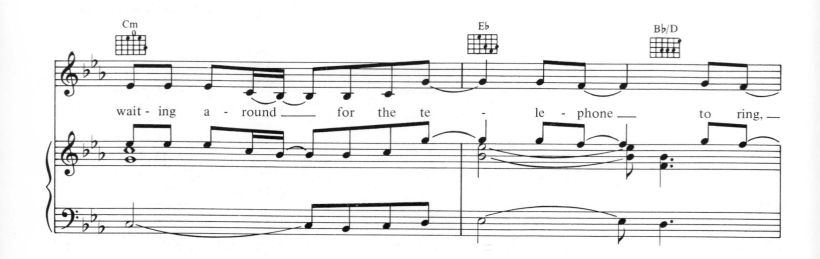

wait-ing a-round ___ for the te - le - phone ___ to ring, ___

47

two of a kind, _____ two of a kind. _____

48

VERSE 2:
You say it's only a matter of time
And there must be someone else
You wanna trust in his promises
But you'll never fool yourself
Now you're reading into his every move
Like he only tells you lies
And then you're on the phone
And he's on his own saying
"Come round tonight, make love to me."

I Listen to the Rain

I listen to the rain whispering your name
And hurricanes cloud my life again.
The memory will fade
And time will turn the page
Our love was made,
I dream of yesterday.

The fantasy is mine
It's you I long to find.

   I close my eyes
   And dream that you are here tonight,
   Make believe you're crazy for me.

You turn your head to hide, I know the reason why,
The moon we ride
Could drown the swelling tide.
I call out from the shore
A siren from the sand
This lonely land I am forever more

The fantasy is mine
It's you I long to find

   I close my eyes
   And dream that you are here tonight

   Make believe you're crazy for me
   I close my eyes
   And dream that you are here tonight
   I listen to the rain
   Whispering your name,
   Whispering your name

I LISTEN TO THE RAIN

Words and Music by
BEVERLEY CRAVEN

cra-zy for me. _____ I close _____ my eyes _____ and dream_____

_____ that you _____ are here _____ to-night, _____ lis - ten to the rain,

whis - per - ing your name, whis - per - ing your name.

VERSE 2:
You turn your head to hide
I know the reason why
The moon we ride
Could drown the swelling tide
I call out from the shore
A siren from the sand
This lonely land, I am forever more.

Missing You

The dreams I have are unrepeatable
And you always play a starring role
I'm just glad to have the time with you
It's the only place where we can go

I walk around the next day in a daze
Flashes of a feeling of your face
Three photographs, a letter and my memories
Are all I have to fill this space

    Now you've gone, now you've gone
    But I keep missing you
    I keep missing you
    Now you've gone, now you've gone
    But I keep missing you
    I keep missing you

Sometimes I laugh the way you used to laugh
Or say the things you used to say
If you can see me now just give me a sign
'Cause I can't believe you've really gone away

    Now you've gone, now you've gone
    But I keep missing you
    I keep missing you
    Now you've gone, now you've gone
    But I keep missing you
    I keep missing you

The way you tossed your hair and fooled around
Will we ever meet again

    Now you've gone, now you've gone
    But I keep missing you
    I keep missing you
    Now you've gone, now you've gone
    But I keep missing you
    I keep missing you

MISSING YOU

Words and Music by
BEVERLEY CRAVEN

VERSE 2:

Sometimes I laugh the way I used to laugh
Or say the things you used to say
If you can see me now
Just give me a sign
'Cause I can't really believe you've gone away.

VERSE 3:

Instrumental 4 bars
The way you tossed your hair
And fooled around
Will we ever meet again.

Printed in England
Panda Press · Haverhill · Suffolk • 11/91